Giant Coloring and Activity Book

To Serve and To Save!

Fisher-Price

Modern Publishing
A Division of Unisystems, Inc.
New York, New York 10022
Series UPC#: 49440
Printed in the U.S.A.

The Rescue Heroes™ Team is always prepared!

Billy Blazes,™ Team Leader

Live Wire!

1. DEDICATED DOG
The Rescue Heroes™ Team has a special helper. Connect the dots from 1 to 40 to reveal this canine companion.

See Answers

START

FINISH

2. IN A HURRY!

There's an emergency in town! Jake Justice™ needs to get to his vehicle quickly! Help him by following the correct path through the maze.

See Answers

Wendy Waters™ to the rescue!

It's Gil Gripper™.

Commitment and unity save lives!

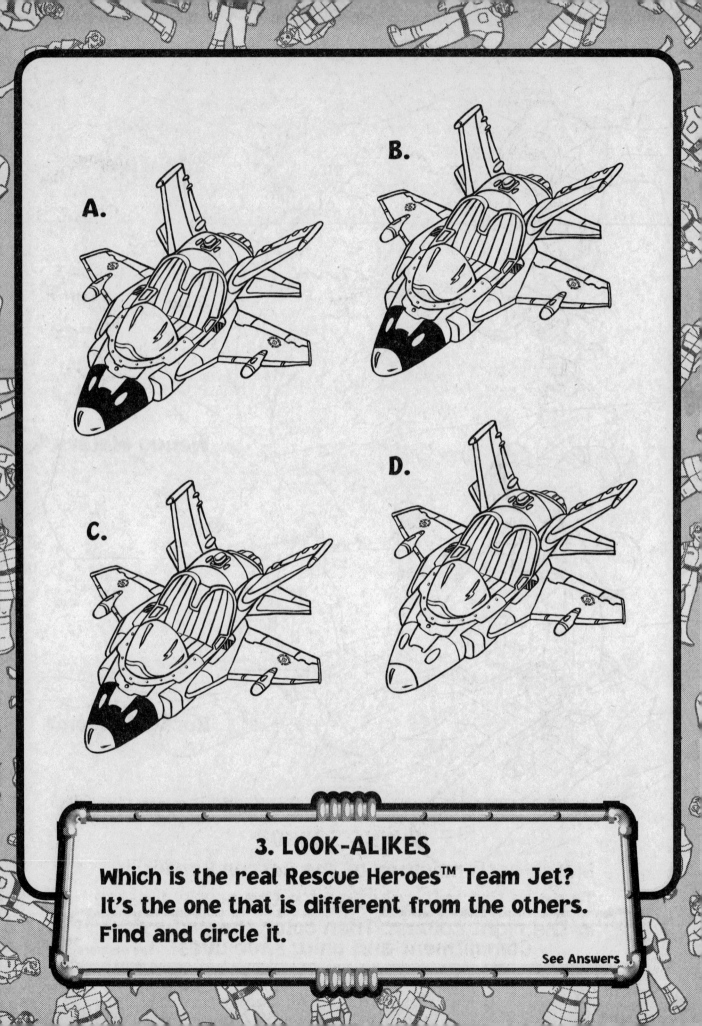

A.

B.

C.

D.

3. LOOK-ALIKES

Which is the real Rescue Heroes™ Team Jet?
It's the one that is different from the others.
Find and circle it.

See Answers

Ariel Flyer™

Billy Blazes™

Wendy Waters™

Jake Justice™

Rocky Canyon™

4. WHO'S WHO?

Match each member of the Rescue Heroes™
Team in the left column with the correct name
in the right column. Then color the pictures.

See Answers

No fire is too big for Billy Blazes™ to handle.

Rocky Canyon's™ hooked on helping people!

"Brush fire alert! If you don't get there soon, the coast will be toast!"

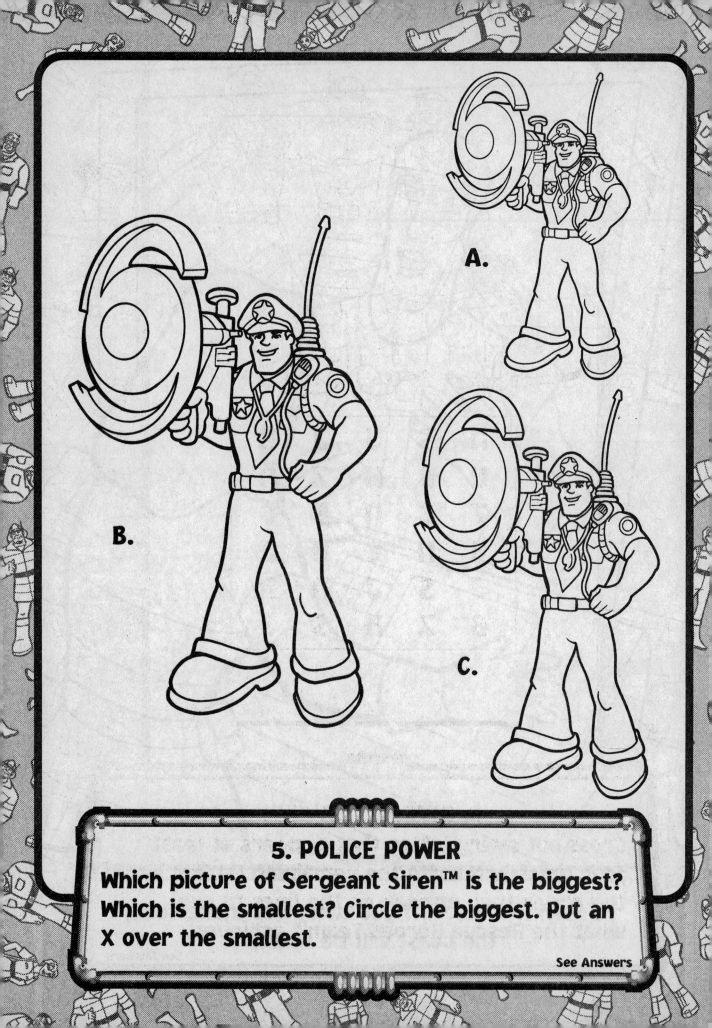

A.

B.

C.

5. POLICE POWER

Which picture of Sergeant Siren™ is the biggest? Which is the smallest? Circle the biggest. Put an X over the smallest.

See Answers

n	S	J	J	B
u	B	H	Z	n
Z	C	n	B	c
H	n	E	H	Z
J	S	J	n	n
B	Z	H	S	J

_ _ _ _ _ _ _ _ _ _

6. GIVE ME AN "S"!
Cross out every letter that appears at least four times and write the remaining letters in the order they appear on the lines to see what the Rescue Heroes Team™ achieves.

See Answers

Wendy Waters'™ water cannon pours it on!

"Get in quick. Get out safe!"

Rocky Canyon™ helps save the day!

The Rescue Heroes™ Team goes mobile!

Gil Gripper™ has a grip on safety!

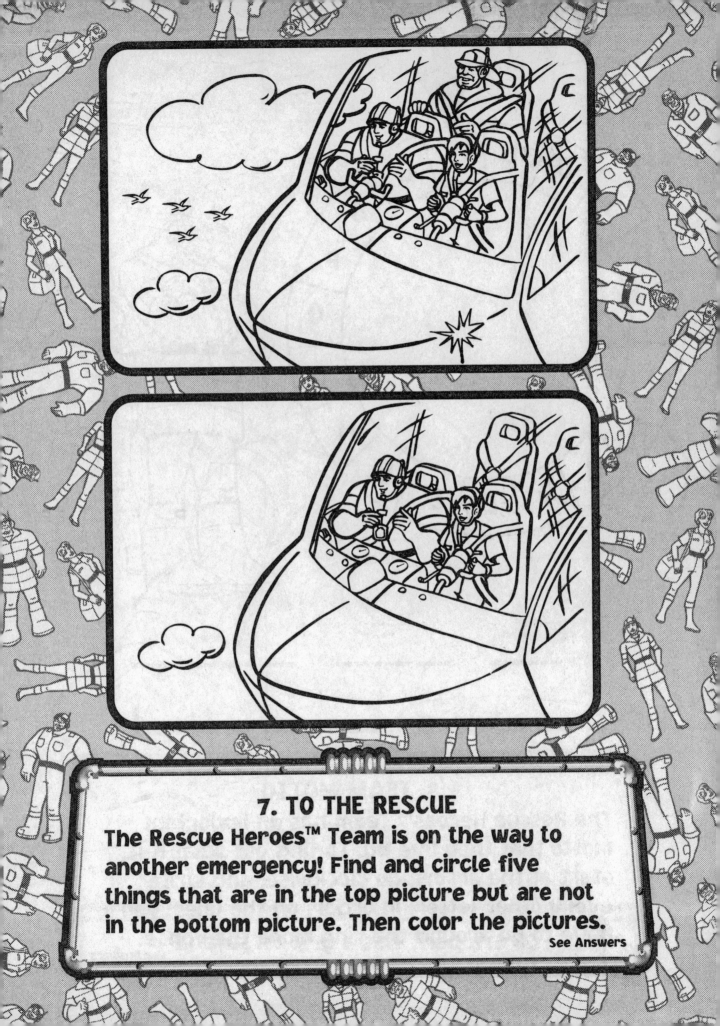

7. TO THE RESCUE
The Rescue Heroes™ Team is on the way to another emergency! Find and circle five things that are in the top picture but are not in the bottom picture. Then color the pictures.

See Answers

_____ _____ _____ _____

_____ _____!

8. TEAM MOTTO

The Rescue Heroes™ Team has an important motto that they live by. To find out what it is, start at the arrow, go clockwise, and write every other letter, in order, on the lines. You'll have to go around the ring more than once.

See Answers

Disaster Watch

Perseverance

Ariel Flyer™—Friend to Animals

Rescue Chopper looks for a lost mountain climber.

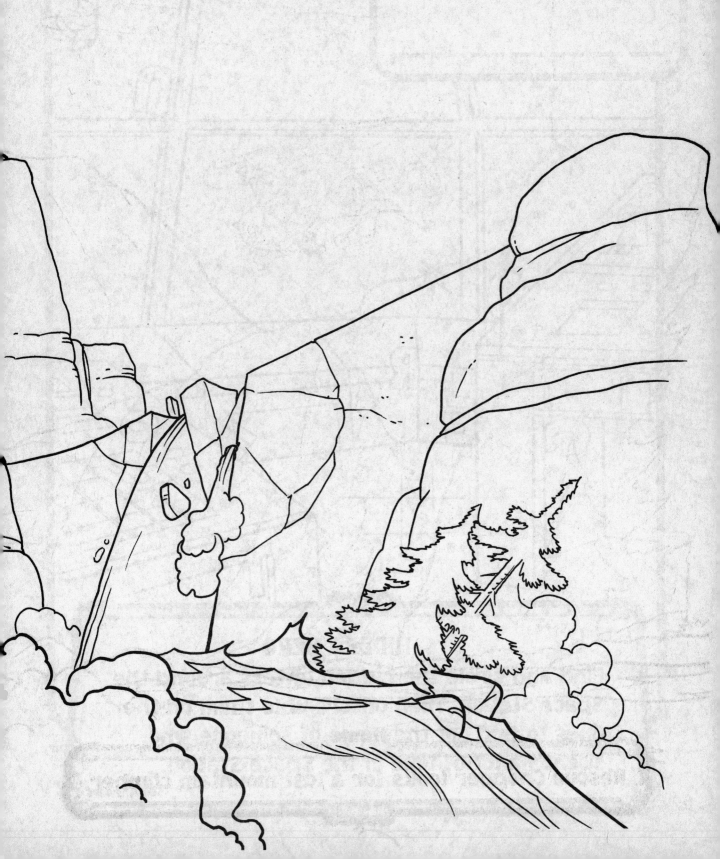

9. HIDDEN HERO

Find and circle the hidden letters around the Space Station. Then unscramble them on the lines to find out the name of someone who spends a lot of time in the Space Station.

See Answers

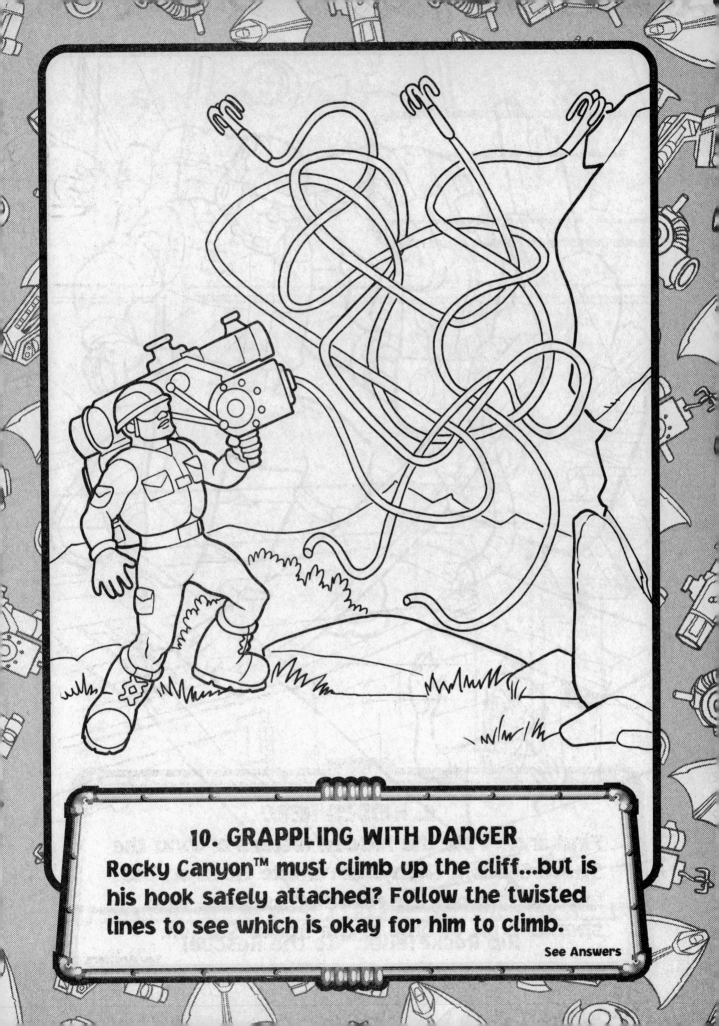

10. GRAPPLING WITH DANGER

Rocky Canyon™ must climb up the cliff...but is his hook safely attached? Follow the twisted lines to see which is okay for him to climb.

See Answers

Rip Rockefeller™ to the Rescue!

"Remember: Don't accept rides from strangers!"

Cycle Specialist

Checking In

Sergeant Siren™ on the Scene

Start

FINISH

11. BILLY BLAZES™ TO THE RESCUE

There's an emergency in town. Help Billy Blazes™ get to the Quick Response Vehicle by following the correct path through the maze.

See Answers

Ariel Flyer™

Billy Blazes™

Wendy Waters™

```
R O C K Y C A N Y O N S
J A K E J U S T I C E E
W E C Z Y A G R Q L N N
K A J A C R E I J H D X
O U K T K I R E W S G Y
P K B V H E T R E W O W
M L O I U L J V C Z Q A
B H I U T F A S D I T B
L Z E D R L U H H R E W
E B I L L Y B L A Z E S
H T C Y M E H K D H U K
O I U Y T R E W Q A V G
W E N D Y W A T E R S J
```

Jake Justice™

Rocky Canyon™

12. A FIRST-RATE TEAM

The Rescue Heroes™ Team members are top-notch pros. Can you find and circle their names in the puzzle grid? Look up, down, and diagonally.

See Answers

Safety Vehicle

Billy Blazes™ and Wendy Waters™ are ready!

Help is on the way!

Gil Gripper™ and Nemo™

Billy Blazes™—Team Leader

13. RESCUE VEHICLE
Draw your own version of the Quick Response Watercraft.

14. NO ONE GETS LEFT BEHIND
Help Ariel Flyer™ and Smokey™ get the animals to safety! Find and circle five hidden animals.

See Answers

Smokey™ is a real hero!

Safety Specialists

Sergeant Siren,™ Courageous Cop

Fire-safety Specialist

No job is too big...

...or too small!

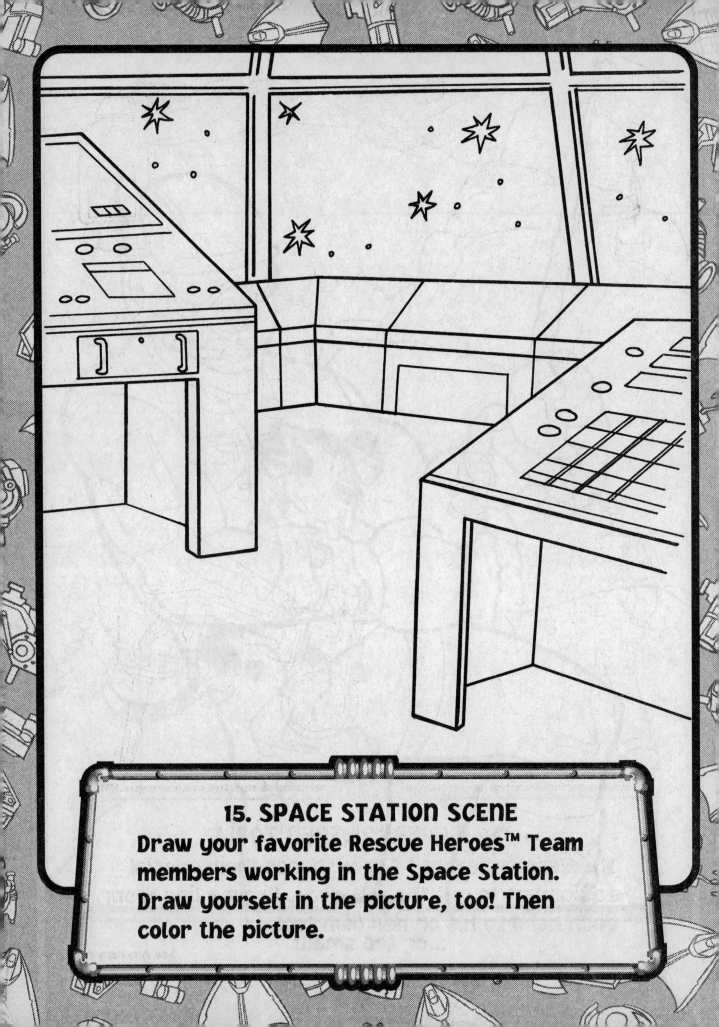

15. SPACE STATION SCENE

Draw your favorite Rescue Heroes™ Team members working in the Space Station. Draw yourself in the picture, too! Then color the picture.

16. SUPERPOWERED TOOLS

The Rescue Heroes™ Team shares their special equipment to get the job done. Draw a line from each hero to his or her own tool.

See Answers

NEIGHBORHOOD SAFETY PLAN

Education saves lives!

A Call to Action

Teamwork

Claude™ the Mountain Lion

S _ n _ Y B _ A C _ ™

R _ C K _ C _ n y _ n ™

B _ L L _ B L _ _ E S ™

See Answers

17. LIFESAVERS
Fill in the missing letters to complete the name of each of the members of the Rescue Heroes™ Team.

START

FINISH

18. AQUATIC ADVENTURE
Gil Gripper™ needs Nemo's™ help. Follow the path with the rescue dolphin's name spelled correctly to lead him to Gil Gripper.™

See Answers

Mission Accomplished!

Billy Blazes™ has a tough job ahead of him!

Gil Gripper™

Smokey™ and Nemo™: Brave Helpers

Sergeant Siren™ is ready for an emergency.

Wendy Waters™ makes sure no one gets left behind!

RESPONSIBILITY

EDUCATION

SAFETY

COMMITMENT

UNITY

ENVIRONMENT

19. DARING DIVER

Connect the dots from 1 to 30 to see the
amazing animal who works with Gil Gripper™.

See Answers

20. SEE THE HERO
Fill in every space with a dot to see this
member of the Rescue Heroes™ Team.

See Answers

Ariel Flyer™

Billy Blazes™

Wendy Waters™

Jake Justice™

Rocky Canyon™

Inbound for Rescue!

Teamwork gets the job done!

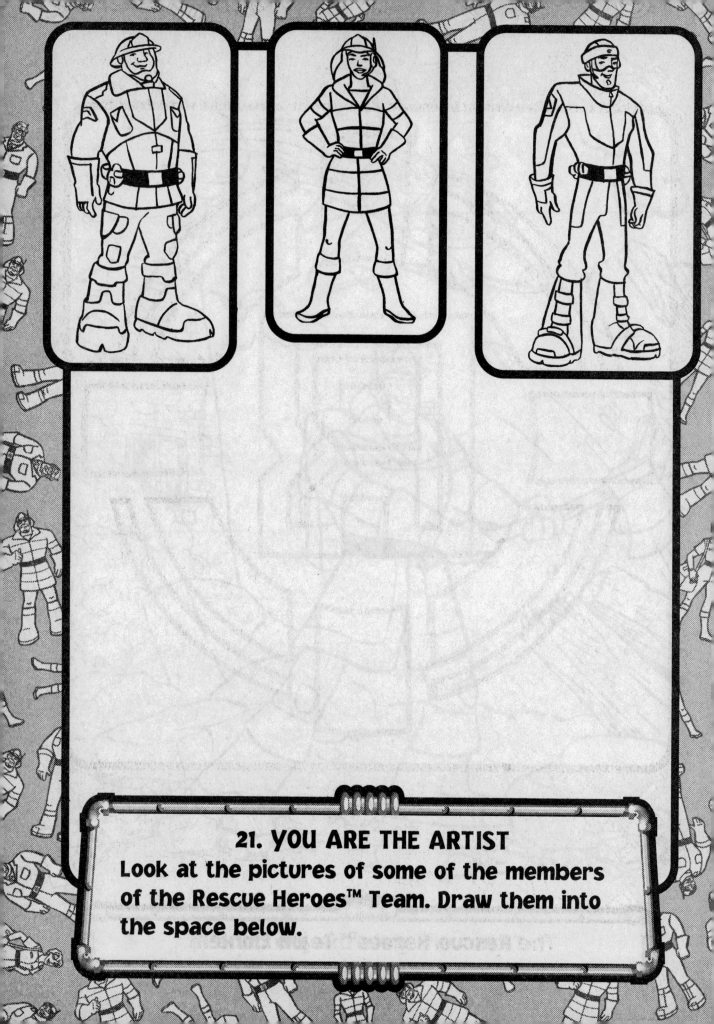

21. YOU ARE THE ARTIST
Look at the pictures of some of the members of the Rescue Heroes™ Team. Draw them into the space below.

The Rescue Heroes™ Team Emblem

These Heroes know the ropes.

Gil Gripper™ is a lifesaver!

Sergeant Siren™ sounds the alarm!

"Take the pledge: Protect the environment!"

22. WHO'S WHO IN HEROES

Draw a line from each picture on the left to the one that is the same on the right.

See Answers

The town is saved!

Helicopter Crash: Civilians in Danger!

Wendy Waters™ has things under control!

23. DOUBLE DUTY
Which two pictures of Sergeant Siren™ are exactly alike? Find and circle them.

See Answers

When there's a flood—call Jack Hammer™.

Start

Finish

24. ON THE WAY
Help the Rescue Heroes™ Team get to the ski resort to warn the skiers about the blizzard by following the correct path through the maze.

See Answers

HELPHERLAPHELDPHEALPHELPHRELGPUHENLPH

__ __ __ __ __ __ __   __ __ __

25. JAKE'S GEAR

Cross out every letter in the word HELP and write the remaining letters in the order they appear on the lines to see what Jake Justice™ carries.

See Answers

Rocky Canyon™ helps save the day!

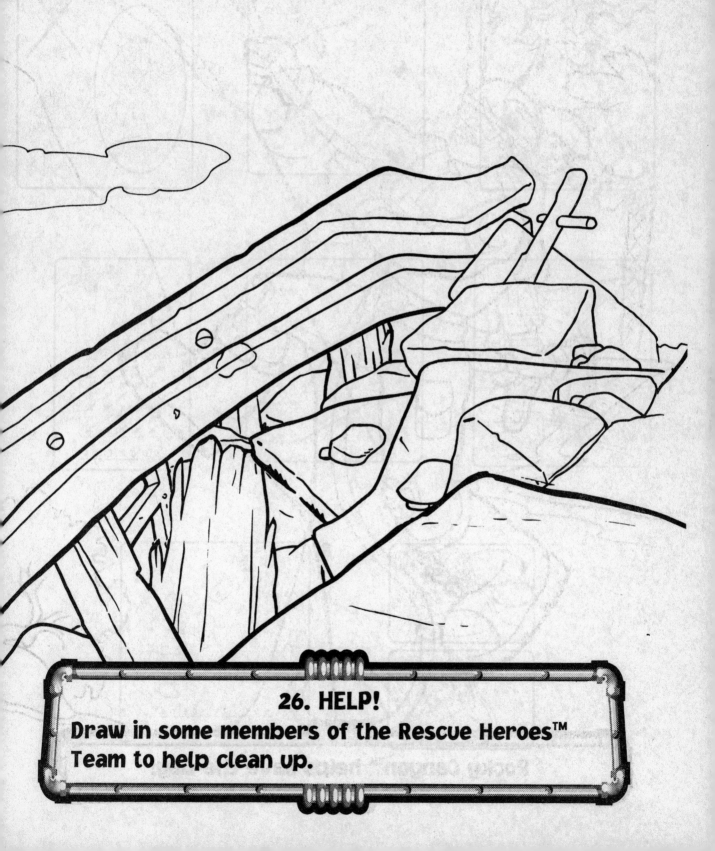

26. HELP!
Draw in some members of the Rescue Heroes™ Team to help clean up.

1.

3.

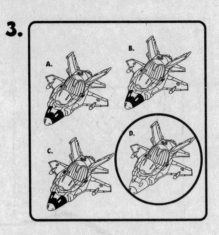

5.

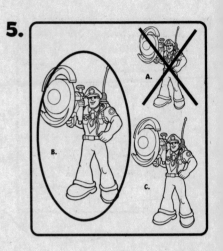

2.

4.

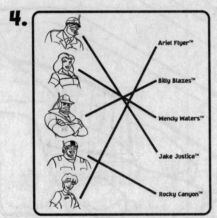

6.

7.

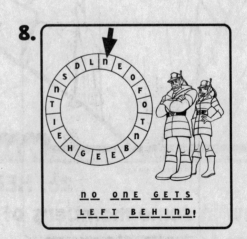

8.

9.

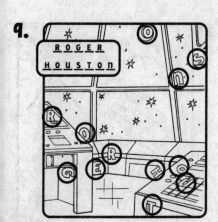

11.

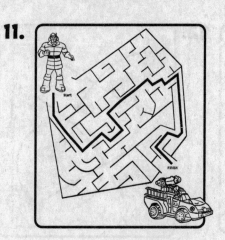

14.

10.

12.

16.

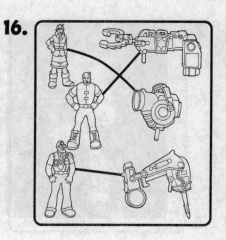

17.

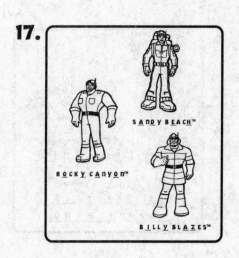

18.

ANSWERS

19.

22.

24.

20.

23.

25.

RADAR GUN